Beginners Book of Bad Behaviour

THE Beginner's Book of Bad Behaviour

OR
A CHILD'S GARDEN OF VICES

Compiled and illustrated
by Colin West

BEAVER BOOKS

A Beaver Book
Published by Arrow Books Limited
62–5 Chandos Place, London WC2N 4NW
An imprint of Century Hutchinson Ltd

London Melbourne Sydney Auckland
Johannesburg and agencies throughout the world

First published by Hutchinson Children's Books 1987
Beaver edition 1989
Copyright © in this edition Colin West 1987
Copyright © Illustrations Colin West 1987

Set in Bembo by Book Ens, Saffron Walden, Essex

Made and printed in Great Britain
by Anchor Press Ltd
Tiptree, Essex

ISBN 0 09 959670 9

The care of books

Don't throw a book down on its face,
But put it in its proper place,
And never leave it on the mat,
Or use it to correct the cat.

Contents

Initials

I think I hardly ever see
Initials carved on fence or tree
Without recalling little Ted,
(Not lost, but gone, alas, ahead),
Who cut, with insufficient thought,
Initials where he didn't ought.
His mother's eldest sister, Kate,
Had given him, to celebrate
The seventh birthday of his life,
A many-bladed pocket-knife,

And this attention to their lad
Made both of Edward's parents glad.
But when his father found, next day,
His pencils sharpened right away,

And Ma had swept, on all her fours,
The whittled wood from several floors,
They sternly told their son, 'You can't
Thus use the penknife of your aunt.
Employ it to some purpose, do,
Or we shall have it took from you.'

So Edward sat him, thinking, down,
And after study long and brown
Bethought, 'I might with profit use
My knife to label which is whose

Of all the miscellaneous lot
Of things my family has got.
There's nothing gives me so the pip
As arguments on ownership.'

Now people suffer deep distress
Who find on objects they possess,
On hats and boots, on books and ties,
Initials of enormous size,

Especially if these are made
By penknife with a bluntish blade,
And Edward's people, by his tricks
Were penetrated to their quicks.
His mother darned with might and main
To mend the damage, but in vain;

For patched and stitched she never so,
The lacerations seemed to grow,
While Pa, who tried percussive force
Upon the problem at its source,
And doubtless left some pretty prints,
Found Edward was opaque to hints.

Of all the Smiths' possessions far
The proudest was their motor-car.
They kept a special little shed
In which it went at night to bed,
With extra super double bars
To outmanoeuvre burglars.
They kept it bright each day with wax,

And even gladly paid its tax,
While so much had it come to be
A member of the family
They suffered nothing to prevent
It going everywhere they went.
Now Ted had heard, in chance remarks,
Of cars abducted from their parks,
And, thinking that it might increase

The chances of the local police,
With open knife to garage sped
And on that motor's outer tread,
Both back and front and off and near,
Incised initials deep and clear.

Next day his Pa and Ma and he
Set out for Southport by the sea,
And Pa, in packing, came upon
Fresh items with initials on.

This caused delay and, hence, a need
For consequently greater speed.
Small wonder as they seaward tore
Those sculptured outer covers wore
And, mid the traffic at its worst,
ALL SIMULTANEOUSLY BURST!

In vain there rose on every side
The awful screech of brakes applied;
That ordered highway had become
A sort of motor rugger scrum
With, in and underneath it all,
Poor Edward's motor as the ball.

Those gentle readers are correct
Who think no person should expect
From such a tangle to contrive
To extricate himself alive.

H.A. Field

The Plum Cake

'Oh! I've got a plum cake, and a rare feast I'll
    make,
I'll eat, and I'll stuff, and I'll cram,
Morning, noontime, and night, it shall be my
    delight,
What a happy young fellow I am!'

Thus said little George, and beginning to gorge,
With zeal to his cake he applied;
While fingers and thumbs, for the sweetmeats
    and plums,
Were hunting and
    digging beside.

But woeful to tell, a misfortune befell,
Which ruined this capital fun;
After eating his fill, he was taken so ill,
That he trembled for what he had done.

As he grew worse and worse, the doctor and
    nurse,
To cure his disorder were sent:
And rightly, you'll think, he had physic to drink,
Which made him his folly repent.

And while on the bed he rolled his hot head,
Impatient with sickness and pain,
He could not but take this reproof from his
    cake:
'Don't be such a glutton again.'

Ann Taylor

18

Cruel John

John was a very naughty boy,
He liked to tease the cat,
To pull her tail when she was sound
Asleep upon the mat.

To chase her down the garden path,
With yells and horrid hoots,
To kick her slyly, though he wore
A pair of hobnailed boots.

He liked to offer bits of bread
And bones to honest Tray;
To hold them to his nose, and then
To snatch the food away.

He liked to beat him with a stick
When nobody was by;
It seemed to give him great delight
To hear the spaniel cry.

If John's Papa had heard of this,
I should not think it odd
If he had taken Master John
And whipped him with a rod.

Because for ugly tricks like these,
To which he was addicted,
John certainly deserved to bear
What often he inflicted.

But one fine day when teasing puss,
And this I mention gladly,
Miss Tabbycat put out her claws
And scratched him very badly.

And quite by accident, I think,
When John came up and hit him,
As he was sleeping in the sun,
Tray snapped at John, and bit him.

John shrieked and screamed because his leg
Hurt very much indeed;
But that it served him right, his friends
Were every one agreed.

Mrs Coxhead

Drawing Teeth

Miss Lucy Wright, though not so tall,
Was just the age of Sophy Ball:
But I have always understood,
Miss Sophy was not half so good;
For as they both had faded teeth,
Their teacher sent for Doctor Heath;
But Sophy made a dreadful rout,
And would not have hers taken out;
But Lucy Wright endured the pain,
Nor did she ever once complain;
Her teeth returned quite sound and white,
While Sophy's ached both day and night.

Elizabeth Turner

A Standing Order

When Mrs Keen commenced to teach
Her infant son the rules of speech,
She started her instructions thus:
'Pray never be ambiguous!

'Of any statement that you make,
Be sure there shall be no mistake,
And be exact in what you mean –
As I, you know, have always been.'

As Johnnie let his doubts appear
At that, his mother boxed his ear,
And in a tone of stern command
Right in the corner bade him stand.

She saw him to his place of doom,
Then rose and gently left the room;
But on returning found instead
Young Johnnie standing on his head.

Amazed at having to detect
A disobedience so direct,
She cried, repeating the command:
'I thought I told you, sir, to *stand*!'

Then, as she waited for a while,
A voice came off the velvet pile:
'You didn't say,' said Master John,
'Which end I was to stand upon.'

Hearing – with meaning misapplied –
Her careful lesson so decried,
His mother picked him up at that,
And whipped him soundly where he sat.

Laurence Housman

Rebecca,

Who slammed Doors for Fun and Perished Miserably

A Trick that everyone abhors
In Little Girls is slamming Doors.
A Wealthy Banker's Little Daughter
Who lived in Palace Green, Bayswater
(By name Rebecca Offendort),
Was given to this Furious Sport.

She would deliberately go
And Slam the door like Billy-Ho!
To make her Uncle Jacob start.
She was not really bad at heart,
But only rather rude and wild:
She was an aggravating child . . .

It happened that a Marble Bust
Of Abraham was standing just
Above the Door this little Lamb

Had carefully prepared to Slam,

And Down it came! It knocked her flat!

It laid her out! She looked like that.

Her funeral Sermon (which was long
And followed by a Sacred Song)
Mentioned her Virtues, it is true,
But dwelt upon her Vices too,
And showed the Dreadful End of One
Who goes and slams the door for Fun.

*

The children who were brought to hear
The awful Tale from far and near
Were much impressed, and inly swore
They never more would slam the Door
– As often they had done before.

Hilaire Belloc

The Children's 'Don't'

Don't tell Papa his nose is red
As any rosebud or geranium;
Forbear to eye his hairless head
Or criticize his cootlike cranium;
'Tis years of sorrow and of care
Have made his head come through his hair.

Don't give your endless guinea-pig
(Wherein that animal may build a
Sufficient nest) the Sunday wig
Of poor, dear, dull, deaf Aunt Matilda;
Oh, *don't* tie strings across her path,
Or empty beetles in her bath!

Don't ask your uncle why he's fat;
Avoid upon his toe-joints treading;
Don't hide a hedgehog in his hat,
Or bury brushes in his bedding.
He will not see the slightest sport
In pepper put into his port!

Don't pull away the cherished chair
On which Mama intended sitting,
Nor yet prepare her session there
By setting on the seat her knitting;
Pause ere you hurt her spine, I pray –
That is a game that *two* can play.

Harry Graham

The Story of Frozen James

What a charming boy was James!
Good at lessons, good at games,
Courteous to his aunts and others,
Patient with his younger brothers . . .

Yet this almost perfect lad
One unholy passion had:
He would think and talk and dream
All day long about ice-cream.

In the middle of the morning
First would come the tinkled warning;
Out he'd rush and gobble up
'Block' and 'cornet', 'brick' and 'cup'.
Then between his lunch and tea
He'd dispose of two or three,
And before the day was done
Manage yet another one.
Foolish child! This chilly diet
Caused his parents much disquiet.
'James,' they said with bated breath,
'Mark our words – you'll freeze to death.'

Parents' warnings (some have found)
Aren't so silly as they sound:
James, ignoring their advice,
One fine day was turned to ice.
What a lamentable plight!
Half was pink and half was white,
While where fingers should have been

Icicles were plainly seen.
'Will the wretched boy expire?
Quickly – we must light a fire!
Henry, fetch some sticks and straw . . .'
Just in time: his parents saw
James at last begin to thaw.

Now once more he's safe and warm,
Quite restored to human form:
But somehow he doesn't seem
Half so partial to ice-cream.

Jan Struther

Sophia's Fool's-cap

Sophia was a little child,
Obliging, good, and very mild,
Yet lest of dress she should be vain,
Mama still dressed her well, but plain.
Her parents, sensible and kind,
Wished only to adorn her mind;
No other dress, when good, had she,
But useful, neat simplicity.
Though seldom, yet when she was rude,
Or ever in a naughty mood,

Her punishment was this disgrace,
A large fine cap, adorned with lace,
With feathers and with ribbons too;
The work was neat, the fashion new,
Yet, as a fool's-cap was its name,
She dreaded much to wear the same.

A lady, fashionably gay,
Did to Mama a visit pay:
Sophia stared, then whisp'ring said,
'Why, dear Mama, look at her head!

To be so tall and wicked too,
The strangest thing I ever knew:
What naughty tricks, pray, has she done,
That they have put that fool's-cap on?'

Adelaide O'Keefe

The Boy who Laughed at Santa Claus

In Baltimore there lived a boy.
He wasn't anybody's joy.
Although his name was Jabez Dawes,
His character was full of flaws.
In school he never led his classes,
He hid old ladies' reading glasses,

His mouth was open when he chewed,
And elbows to the table glued.
He stole the milk of hungry kittens,
And walked through doors marked NO
    ADMITTANCE.
He said he acted thus because
There wasn't any Santa Claus.

Another trick that tickled Jabez
Was crying 'Boo!' at little babies.
He brushed his teeth, they said in town,
Sideways instead of up and down.

Yet people pardoned every sin,
And viewed his antics with a grin,
Till they were told by Jabez Dawes,
'There isn't any Santa Claus!'

Deploring how he did behave,
His parents swiftly sought their grave.
They hurried through the portals pearly,
And Jabez left the funeral early.

Like whooping cough, from child to child,
He sped to spread the rumour wild:
'Sure as my name is Jabez Dawes
There isn't any Santa Claus!'

Slunk like a weasel or a marten
Through nursery and kindergarten,
Whispering low to every tot,
'There isn't any, no there's not!'

The children wept all Christmas Eve
And Jabez chortled up his sleeve.
No infant dared hang up his stocking
For fear of Jabez' ribald mocking.

He sprawled on his untidy bed,
Fresh malice dancing in his head,
When presently with scalp-a-tingling,
Jabez heard a distant jingling;
He heard the crunch of sleigh and hoof
Crisply alighting on the roof.

What good to rise and bar the door?
A shower of soot was on the floor.
What was beheld by Jabez Dawes?
The fireplace full of Santa Claus!

Then Jabez fell upon his knees
With cries of 'Don't,' and 'Pretty please.'
He howled, 'I don't know where you read it,
But anyhow, I never said it!'

'Jabez,' replied the angry saint,
'It isn't I, it's you that ain't.
Although there is a Santa Claus,
There isn't any Jabez Dawes!'
Said Jabez then with impudent vim,
'Oh, yes, there is, and I am him!
Your magic don't scare me, it doesn't' –
And suddenly he found he wasn't!

From grimy feet to grimy locks,
Jabez became a Jack-in-the-box,
An ugly toy with springs unsprung,
Forever sticking out his tongue.

The neighbours heard his mournful squeal;
They searched for him, but not with zeal.

No trace was found of Jabez Dawes,
Which led to thunderous applause,
And people drank a loving cup
And went and hung their stockings up.

All you who sneer at Santa Claus,
Beware the fate of Jabez Dawes,
The saucy boy who mocked the saint.
Donner and *Blitzen* licked off his paint.

Ogden Nash

The Wrong Way to
Stroke a Tiger

Oh list to the story of Mrs Wynne-Porter,
Whose recklessness caused her regrettable
    slaughter;
She loved to stroke tigers, she did, the wrong
    way!
A habit which filled all her friends with dismay.

They warned her in Latin, they warned her in
    Greek,
And on Tuesday and Friday every week;
They warned her in English, they warned her
    in French,
But failed altogether her ardour to quench.

'The tiger,' they said, 'is a querulous beast,
Whom incorrect stroking can't please in the
    least,
It ruffles his temper, it ruffles his fur,
We've no wish to offend you but really you
    err.'

But Mrs Wynne-Porter, regretful to say,
Only sniffed in a very superior way,
And made it her practice after each warning,
To visit the jungle the very next morning.

And at dinner she'd boast to her friends at the
club,
'I've had a good day, I've stroked two, and a
cub';
While lamenting her rashness and stubbornness
glaring,
One has to admit that the lady was daring.

But at last came the day when she made a
bungle,
And failed to return from her stroll in the
jungle.
A false tooth, a pink garter, four beads from
her necklace,
Were the sole relics left of this lady so reckless.

49

So if *you* chance to dwell near where tigers exist,
From the folly of Mrs Wynne-Porter desist.
But if tigers you *must* stroke – well, then,
   without fail,
The practice perform from the head to the tail.

Langford Reed

The Good Scholar Fights

One afternoon as Joseph West,
The boy who learnt his lesson best,
Was trying how his whip would crack,
By chance he hit Sam Headstrong's back.

Enraged, he flew, and gave poor Joe,
With all his might, a sudden blow:
Nor would he listen to one word,
When Joe endeavoured to be heard.

Joe, finding him resolved to fight,
For what was accidental quite,
Although he never fought before,
Beat Headstrong till he'd have no more.

Elizabeth Turner

The Night Wanderer

When other children were asleep
Our Oswald down the stairs would creep,
And to the fields he'd steal away,
Quite slyly by himself to play.
Sometimes he took the powder-horn,
And with the powder burnt the corn;

Sometimes he hid behind a tree,
And rushing out quite suddenly,
Would make a loud and fearful cry,
And frighten all the passers-by.
Indeed, it was his chief delight
To run away from home at night.
His parents shook their heads, and said,
'Oh! Oswald, stay at home in bed,

For if you out at night do roam
A bat you surely will become.'
But all their talking was in vain;
Still Oswald would go out again.
But, oh! just as his friends had said,
One night, as round the fields he sped,
Upon him came a wondrous change;
'Ah, me!' he cried, 'How very strange
I feel that I become so small,
And now I cannot walk at all.
I put my hands up to my head,

But find a bat's face in its stead;
And now my hands are gone. Oh, dear!
Instead of arms what have I here?

Such very, very curious things.
Why! Can they be? Oh, yes, they're wings.

Alas! Alas! What shall I do?
My parents' words are coming true.
An ugly bat I have become,
And never more shall I go home.'

Oh! yes, my dears, it was too true;
An ugly bat away he flew;

His parents' tears streamed down like rain;
They never saw their child again.

Anon

Mary-Jane and Emily,

Whose viewing habits came unstuck

I wonder if you've been to tea
With Mary-Jane and Emily,
Twin sisters both with golden curls,
The prettiest of little girls?

They're similar in many ways –
Not least in how their tempers blaze.
At tea-time, far from eating food,
The twins are resolutely glued
To television, when they fight
For what they're going to watch that night.
They never ever can agree
Upon which programme they will see.

They pull each other's hair about
And scratch and kick and sulk and pout.
Then one day, Emily let fly –
She hit her sister in the eye
Because she wanted 'Tom and Jerry'.
Gracious! Her vocabulary!
Mary-Jane picked up the jelly,
Missed her sister, hit the telly.
SPLAT! It landed on the screen.
(A pity. It was tangerine.)

Unfortunately, some of it
Ran down inside a tiny slit
And there coagulated, which
Jammed up the programme-channel switch.
The telly stayed for ever more
Immovably on Channel Four.

The sisters went to see their Mum.
'Please ask the engineer to come!'

He came, he saw, and then enquired,
'I s'pose you know this thing is hired?
You can't throw jelly at a box!
At least, it's most unorthodox,'
A word that made the sisters gasp.
(Its meaning's *still* beyond their grasp.)

The man was really most irate
And said, 'I'm going to confiscate
The television set right now –
This sort of thing we can't allow.'
And there and then, without delay,
He took the wretched thing away.

Poor Emily and Mary-Jane
Have never had a fight again.
They have to *talk* and *read* instead,
And go *much* earlier to bed.

The moral here is plain to see:
Don't watch the box while having tea.

Jeremy Nicholas

Mischief

Let those who're fond of idle tricks,
Of throwing stones, and hurling bricks
And all that sort of fun,
Now hear a tale of idle Jim,
That warning they may take by him,
Nor do as he has done.

In harmless sport or healthful play
He did not pass his time away,
Nor took his pleasure in it;
For mischief was his only joy:
No book, or work, nor even toy,
Could please him for a minute.

A neighbour's house he'd slyly pass,
And throw a stone to break the glass,
And then enjoy the joke!
Or, if a window open stood,
He'd throw in stones, or bits of wood,
To frighten all the folk.

If travellers passing chanced to stay,
Of idle Jim to ask the way,
He never told them right;
And then, quite hardened in his sin,
Rejoiced to see them taken in,
And laughed with all his might.

He'd tie a string across the street,
Just to entangle people's feet,
And make them tumble down:
Indeed, he was disliked so much,
That no good boy would play with such
A nuisance to the town.

At last the neighbours in despair,
This mischief would no longer bear:
And so – to end the tale,
This lad, to cure him of his ways,
Was sent to spent some dismal days
Within the county jail.

Jane Taylor

Playing with Fire-arms

A little girl and boy one day,
Were shut into a room to play,
Sometimes they tossed a feather ball,
Or, 'whoop, whoop,' would in hiding call.

But William tired of that at last,
His eyes upon the sideboard cast,
'Oh, there are pistols here I vow,
We'll play at soldiers, Clara, now!'

'No, no,' cried Clara, much afraid,
'You know how oft Mama has said,
We must not in our pastime, such
As knives, or swords, or pistols touch.'

'You silly girl, what needless fear!'
Cried William. 'Pray would they be here
If they were loaded; why you know
Your father never leaves them so!'

With these words, in his sister's hand,
He forced the weapon, and they stand
Apart to take the mimic aim,
He purposed, in his dangerous game.

'Hold up your head,' he cried, 'and be
A soldier, Clara, just like me,
Stand there now, and when I desire,
Look full at me, present, and fire!'

Alas! too true an aim they took,
A dreadful noise the dwelling shook,
The triggers were drawn all too well,
And dead upon the floor they fell.

The noise appalled their mother's ears,
Who runs down in distracting fears,
But even on the threshold lay,
Poor Clara's body in her way.

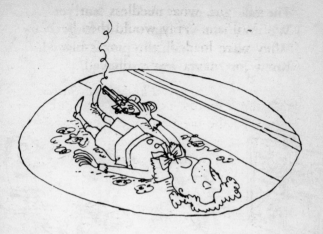

Shot like his sister through the head
The boy, too, on the rug lay dead;
Their mother at this ghastly sight,
Fainted with anguish, and affright.

Dear children! let this dreadful tale
To warn you of such tricks avail,
As cost those little ones their lives,
Then touch not pistols, forks, or knives!

'Tis true that much befitting blame,
Upon the careless servant came,
Who left charged pistols in the way,
Of little children in their play.

The man we may condemn, but yet
We must not William's fault forget,
Who when he with the pistols played,
Knew his Mama was disobeyed.

Elizabeth M. Stewart

Maria and the Inks

Maria was a wicked minx,
With mischief always in her head.
She filled the milk-jug up with inks
(Two kinds: the blue-black and the red).

With fury loud her father roared,
When in his tea, that afternoon,
The mixture horrible was poured!
He guessed the perpetrator soon.

'Abominable child!' he said,
'I'll punish you for acting so!'
He seized Maria by the head,
And shook her fiercely to and fro.

In vain she tried away to slip,
In vain she strove to twist and squirm,
He held her with a mighty grip,
He held her very tight and firm.

What did he do, then, do you think?
Regardless of his daughter's shrieks,
He poured upon her head the ink
Till she was red and black in streaks.

Edith F. B. MacAlister

The Story of Disobedient David

Young David was forbidden quite
To play with the electric light,
But when he asked the reason why,
He got this very strange reply:
'Two hundred volts,' his father said,
'Are quite enough to kill you dead.'

'But what *are* volts?' the boy enquired.
'Don't worry, child! Your father's tired.'

Now David, who was rash and bold
And seldom did what he was told,
At once determined to find out
What all this fuss could be about.
His pocket-knife he quickly drew
And cut the electric wire in two.

Imprudent boy! A monstrous spark
Flew out at him – then all was dark.
Poor David shrieked in wild alarm,
For through his hand and up his arm
Two hundred raging demons leapt,
And pinched and pricked him till he wept.
Blindly he stumbled from the room:
He could not dodge this dreadful doom.

All over him the demons clung
And mercilessly stabbed and stung;
With horrid glee and fiendish grins
They plied their little red-hot pins.

They drove him, howling, down the stairs
And out into the streets and squares,
And people wondered, as he passed,
How any boy could run so fast.

His parents searched for him in vain:
David was never seen again.
So now they sit (unhappy sight!)
And mourn their loss – by candle-light.

Jan Struther

Vain Victor

Victor was so very vain,
Oft he gave his mother pain;
'Oh!' she cried, 'what shall we do
With a peacock-boy like you?'
Vain of this and vain of that,
Of his Sunday clothes and hat,
Warned again, and yet again,
Still he went on being vain!

Soon a change came over him,
Both in feature and in limb;
He grew much too vain to speak,
Then came feathers, tail, and beak!

After this, so I have learned,
He into a peacock turned.
Boys and girls, take warning, do,
Lest you turn to peacocks too!

Clifton Bingham

Kenneth,

Who was too fond of bubble-gum and met an untimely end

The chief defect of Kenneth Plumb
Was chewing too much bubble-gum.
He chewed away with all his might,
Morning, evening, noon and night.
Even (oh, it makes you weep)
Blowing bubbles in his sleep.

He simply couldn't get enough!
His face was covered with the stuff.
As for his teeth – oh, what a sight!
It was a wonder he could bite.
His loving mother and his dad
Both remonstrated with the lad.

Ken repaid them for the
    trouble
By blowing yet another
    bubble.

'Twas no joke. It isn't funny
Spending all your pocket money
On the day's supply of gum –
Sometimes Kenny felt quite glum.
As he grew, so did his need –
There seemed no limit to his greed:
At ten he often put away
Ninety-seven packs a day.

Then at last he went too far –
Sitting in his father's car,
Stuffing gum without a pause,
Found that he had jammed his jaws.
He nudged his dad and pointed to

The mouthful that he couldn't chew.
'Well, spit it out if you can't chew it!'
Ken shook his head. He couldn't do it.
Before long he began to groan –
The gum was solid as a stone.
Dad took him to a builder's yard;

They couldn't help. It was too hard.

They called a doctor and he said,
'This silly boy will soon be dead.
His mouth's so full of bubble-gum
No nourishment can reach his tum.'

Remember Ken and please do not
Go buying too much you-know-what.

Wendy Cope

The Story of Fidgety Philip

'Let me see if Philip can
Be a little gentleman;
Let me see if he is able
To sit still for once at table':
Thus Papa bade Phil behave;
And Mama looked very grave.
But fidgety Phil,
He won't sit still;
He wriggles,
He giggles,
And then, I declare,

Swings backwards and forwards,
And tilts up his chair,
Just like any rocking horse –
'Philip! I am getting cross!'

See the naughty, restless child
Growing still more rude and wild,

Till his chair falls over quite.
Philip screams with all his might,
Catches at the cloth, but then
That makes matters worse again.
Down upon the ground they fall,
Glasses, plates, knives, forks, and all.
How Mama did fret and frown,
When she saw them tumbling down!
And Papa made such a face!
Philip is in sad disgrace.

Where is Philip, where is he?
Fairly covered up you see!

Cloth and all are lying on him;
He has pulled down all upon him.
What a terrible to-do!
Dishes, glasses snapped in two!
Here a knife, and there a fork!
Philip, this is cruel work.
Table all so bare, and ah!
Poor Papa, and poor Mama
Look quite cross, and wonder how
They shall have their dinner now.

Dr Heinrich Hoffmann

Archibald's Progress

Archibald liked pulling faces:
All day long he'd make grimaces,
And at school he'd taunt his teachers
With contortions of his features.

Sitting at his school desk smugly,
Once he pulled a face so ugly,
That he gave poor Miss McKenzie
Cause to fly into a frenzy:

Mouth wide open – how
  revolting!
Tongue protruding – how
  insulting!
Puffed out cheeks and
  wrinkled forehead –
Archibald looked really
  horrid!

Thus it was the nasty creature
So provoked his gentle teacher,
That she, driven to distraction,
Took at once most drastic action.

Pelting him with books, she dented
Archie's head till he repented,
And agreed, that when at places
Such as school, to not pull faces.

Let us now praise Miss McKenzie,
She who flew into a frenzy,
And in just one scripture session,
Made a permanent impression.

Colin West

Jim,

Who ran away from his Nurse and was eaten by a lion

There was a Boy whose name was Jim;
His Friends were very good to him.
They gave him Tea, and Cakes, and Jam,
And slices of delicious Ham,
And Chocolate with pink inside,
And little Tricycles to ride,

And read him Stories through and through,
And even took him to the Zoo –
But there it was the dreadful Fate
Befell him, which I now relate.

You know – at least you *ought* to know,
For I have often told you so –
That Children never are allowed
To leave their Nurses in a Crowd;
Now this was Jim's especial Foible,
He ran away when he was able,
And on this inauspicious day
He slipped his hand and ran away!
He hadn't gone a yard when –

Bang!

With open Jaws, a Lion sprang,
And hungrily began to eat
The Boy: beginning at his feet.

Now just imagine how it feels
When first your toes and then your heels,
And then by gradual degrees,
Your shins and ankles, calves and knees,
Are slowly eaten, bit by bit.
No wonder Jim detested it!

No wonder that he shouted 'Hi!'
The Honest Keeper heard his cry,
Though very fat he almost ran
To help the little gentleman.
'Ponto!' he ordered as he came
(For Ponto was the Lion's name),
'Ponto!' he cried, with angry Frown.
'Let go, Sir! Down, Sir! Put it down!'
The Lion made a sudden Stop,
He let the Dainty Morsel drop,
And slunk reluctant to his Cage,
Snarling with Disappointed Rage

But when he bent him over Jim,
The Honest Keeper's Eyes were dim.
The Lion having reached his Head,
The Miserable Boy was Dead!

When Nurse informed his Parents, they
Were more Concerned than I can say –
His Mother, as She dried her eyes,
Said, 'Well – it gives me no surprise,
He would not do as he was told!'
His Father, who was self-controlled,
Bade all the children round attend
To James's miserable end,
And always keep a-hold of Nurse
For fear of finding something worse.

Hilaire Belloc

The Busy Child

Hannah, a busy meddling thing,
Would peep in every place;
A habit which must always bring
Young folks into disgrace.

One day, her mother put a jar
Upon a cupboard shelf;
Sly Hannah viewed it from afar,
And said within herself,

'What can Mama have placed so high?
It must be something nice,
And, if I thought she were not nigh,
Would see it in a trice.'

Quick on the table then she skipped,
When feeling some alarm,
She sudden turned, her left foot slipped,
She fell – and broke her arm.

Mary Belson

Cruel Tommy

Tom sat at the parlour window,
Watching the people go by;
But what was he really after?
Why, plucking the legs from a fly.

Ay, there he sat in the sunshine,
Tormenting the tiny things;
First plucking their legs from their sockets,
Then afterwards clipping their wings.

He didn't know that his father
Was standing behind his back,
Inclined very much to be giving
His mischievous fingers a crack.

But he waited till after dinner,
When Tommy was having his game,
Then he thought he would give him a lesson,
And treat him a *little* the same.

So catching his son of a sudden,
And giving his elbow a twist,
He pulled at his ear till he holloed,
Then doubled him up with his fist.

And didn't he twist on the carpet,
And didn't he bellow with pain!
But whenever he cried 'Oh, you hurt me!'
His father would punch him again.

'Why, Tom, how amazingly funny!
You don't seem to like it, my boy,
And yet, when you try it on others,
You always are singing for joy.

'It's certainly strange,' said his father;
And this time his nose had a pull;
But Tommy could stand it no longer,
He bellowed and roared like a bull.

'Hush! Hush! while I pull both your legs off,
And clip off the half of each arm;
What you practise yourself, sure, in others
You can't think a sin and a harm.

'Now, Tommy, my boy,' said his father,
'You'll leave these poor creatures alone?
If not, I'll go on with my lesson.'
'I will,' cried poor Tom, with a groan.

Matthias Barr

Dirty Dick

A sadder fate than that of Dick
'Twould puzzle you to find:
He said that water made him sick,
And dirt he didn't mind.

He never washed his hands or face,
Nor had a bath like you;
But dirty went about the place,
And gloried in it too!

At last his parents found one night
(It made them very sad),
In him, with all his dirt, they quite
A kitchen-garden had.

Potatoes from his fingers sprout,
And green stuff from his toes;
And water-cress all round about
His neck and shoulders grows!

Clifton Bingham

The Greedy, Impatient Girl

'Oh! I am so hungry, I'm sure I can't wait
For my apple-pudding to cool,
So, Mary, be quick now, and bring me a plate,
For waiting for dinner I always did hate,
Though forced oft to do it at school.

'But at home, when Mama is not in the way,
I surely will do as I choose;
And I do not care for what you please to say –
The pudding won't burn me – no longer I'll
    stay,
What business have you to refuse?'

And now a large slice of the pudding she got,
And, fearful she should have no more,
She crammed her mouth full of the apple so
   hot,
Which had but a minute come out of the pot,
But quickly her triumph was o'er.

Her mouth and her tongue were so dreadfully
   sore,
And suffered such terrible pain,
Her pride and her consequence soon were all
   o'er,
And she said, now unable to eat any more,
'Oh! I never will do so again.'

And thus by not minding what she had been
    told,
Young Ellinor lost all her treat;
Too greedy to wait till the pudding was cold,
By being impatient, conceited, and bold,
Not a mouthful at last could she eat.

Miss Horwood

Idle Fritz

Fritz was an idle boy, indeed;
He would not learn to write or read;
An ugly face he always made;
His parents, too, he disobeyed;
And mischief was the chief employ
Of this poor, foolish, idle boy.
Look at this picture now, my dear,
And see what he is doing here;

He holds his sister by the braid,
And beats the frightened little maid.
She begs, her tears flow down like rain;
Fritz only laughs to see her pain.

This cat and bird, here lying dead,
He caught and knocked them on the head.

He took from off the fence a rail,
And tied it to poor Carlo's tail;

And, oh! 'twould take me many days
To tell you all his wicked ways.
He for his parents nothing cared,
Therefore, to cure him they despaired;
And, finding they could bear no more,
They whipped and drove him from their door.

'Twas wintertime – the snow fell fast,
And fiercely blew the wintry blast;
Fritz shook with cold from head to toe,
And knew not now where he should go.
But presently a cave he spied;
'Oh! there I'll refuge take,' he cried.
Alas! alas! he did not know
That there he'd meet a cruel foe.
A wolf had made this cave his den;
Fritz never saw the light again.

Anon

Matilda

Matilda got her stockings wet,
And the result was, I regret,
Because she wouldn't change when told,
Matilda caught a dreadful cold.
Matilda sniffed and snuffled and sneezed,
Matilda choked and croaked and wheezed,
And the doctor came, and the doctor said
Matilda was to go to bed.

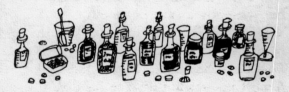

He sent her pills and he sent her potions,
He sent her lozenges and lotions,
Some to be taken straight away,
And others three times every day,
With iodine to paint her skin,
And embrocation to rub in:
In fact, you might almost have filled a
Cart with the things he sent Matilda.

And yet Matilda, if you please,
Disliked the doctor's remedies.
Oh dear! there was a dreadful scene
Each time Matilda took quinine:
Matilda's yells came fast and faster
When they put on a mustard plaster:
Matilda's screams were even louder
When she was given Gregory's powder,
And it took half an hour's toil
To make her swallow castor oil.

I have known other painful cases,
But never seen such awful faces
As those that young Matilda made
On every visit the doctor paid.
What can you do with so self-willed a
Person as the girl Matilda?

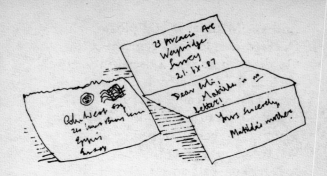

The other day I had a letter
To say Matilda was no better;
And from the way that she's behaving
Matilda doesn't seem worth saving.
Unless Matilda mends her ways
Upon the tombstone that they raise
Will be the words: 'Here lies Matilda.
Nothing but naughty temper killed her.'

F. Gwynne Evans

Dreams

If children have been good all day,
And kept their tongues and lips quite clean,
They dream of flowers that nod and play,
And fairies dancing on the green.

But if they've spoken naughty words,
Or told a lie, they dream of rats:
Of crawling snakes, and ugly birds;
Of centipedes, and vampire bats.

Gabriel Setoun

Acknowledgements

I would like to thank the following poets for material used in this anthology. I hope those earnest Nineteenth Century authors will forgive me if I have illustrated their work somewhat frivolously. I would also like to thank all publishers concerned for originally making the work available. For copyright material, I would like to thank those publishers for permission to reproduce the same. If notified of any omissions, the editor and publisher will gladly make the proper corrections for future editions.

Anon: 'The Night Wanderer' and 'Idle Fritz' from *Simple Hans and Other Funny Pictures and Stories*, T. Nelson & Sons, *c*. 1870.

Matthias Barr: 'Cruel Tommy' from *Hours of Sunshine*, James Nisbet & Co., *c*. 1899.

Hilaire Belloc: 'Rebecca' and 'Jim' from *Cautionary Tales for Children*, reprinted by permission of Gerald Duckworth & Co. Ltd.

Mary Belson: 'The Busy Child' from *Simple Truths*, W. Darton, 1816.

Clifton Bingham: 'Dirty Dick' and 'Vain Victor' from *Six and Twenty Boys and Girls*, Blackie & Son, *c*. 1905.

Wendy Cope: 'Kenneth' reprinted by permission of Faber and Faber Ltd from uncollected poems by Wendy Cope.

Mrs Coxhead: 'Cruel John' from *New Cautionary Rhymes for Children*, Grant Richards, 1903.

F. Gwynne Evans: 'Matilda' from *Puffin, Puma & Co.*, Macmillan & Co., 1929. Reprinted by permission of Macmillan, London and Basingstoke.

H.A. Field: 'Initials' included in *Yet More Comic and Curious Verse*, edited by J.M. Cohen, Penguin Books Ltd, 1959.

Harry Graham: 'The Children's Don't' from *Ruthless Rhymes for Heartless Homes*, reprinted by permission of Edward Arnold (Publishers) Ltd.

Dr Heinrich Hoffmann: 'The Story of Fidgety Philip' from *Struwwelpeter*, Blackie and Son Ltd, 1903.

Miss Horwood: 'The Greedy Impatient Girl' from *Original Poetry for Young Minds*, A.K. Newman & Co., 1822.

Laurence Houseman: 'A Standing Order' from *The New Child's Guide to Knowledge*, Sidgwick & Jackson Ltd, 1911. Reprinted by permission of the publishers.

Edith F.B. MacAlister: 'Maria and the Inks' from *The Misdeeds of Maria*, Hodder and Stoughton Ltd, *c.* 1925.

Ogden Nash: 'The Boy Who Laughed at Santa Claus' from *Custard and Company*, Copyright © 1937 by Ogden Nash. Copyright © renewed 1965 by Ogden Nash. First appeared in *Ladies Home Journal*. Reproduced by permission of Curtis Brown Ltd, London, and Little, Brown and Company, USA.

Jeremy Nicholas: 'Mary-Jane and Emily' from *Raspberries and Other Trifles*, Hutchinson, 1984. Reprinted by permission of Century Hutchinson Ltd.

Adelaide O'Keefe, 'Sophia's Fool's-Cap' from *Original Poems for Infant Minds*, Darton and Harvey, 1804.

Langford Reed: 'The Wrong Way to Stroke a Tiger' from *Sausages and Sundials*, Jarrolds, *c.* 1930. Reprinted by permission of Ms Joan Langford Reed.

Gabriel Setoun: 'Dreams' from *The Child World*, J. Lane, 1898. (Included in *Little Wide-Awake*, edited by Leonard De Vries, Arthur Barker Ltd, 1967.)

Elizabeth M. Stewart: 'Playing With Fire-Arms' from

Original Poetry for Young Persons, Thomas Allman, 1846.

Jan Struther: 'The Story of Frozen James' and 'The Story of Disobedient David' *c*.1936. Reprinted by permission of Punch.

Ann and Jane Taylor: 'The Plum Cake' and 'Mischief' from *Original Poems for Infant Minds*. Darton and Harvey, 1804.

Elizabeth Turner: 'The Good Scholar Fights', and 'Drawing Teeth' from *Mrs Turner's Cautionary Stories*, Grant and Richards, 1897. (Originally published *c*. 1810.)

Colin West: 'Archibald's Progress'. Reprinted by permission of the author.